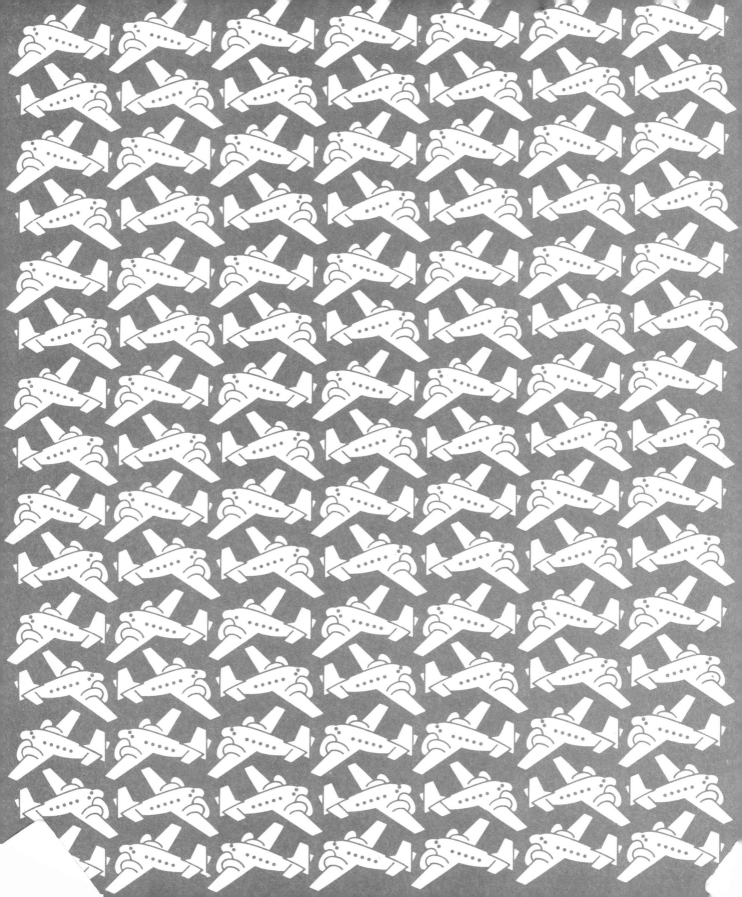

Flying

Donald Crews

SCHOLASTIC INC.
New York   Toronto   London   Auckland   Sydney

ISBN 0-590-46364-0

Copyright © 1986 by Donald Crews.

All rights reserved. Published by Scholastic Inc., 730 Broadway, New York, NY 10003, by arrangement with Greenwillow Books, a division of William Morrow and Company, Inc.

12 11 10 9 8 7 6

Printed in the U.S.A.

First Scholastic printing, February 1993

Gouache paints and an airbrush were used for the full-color art. The typeface is Helvetica Black Italic.

For those who make my heart soar.

06 05 04

24

Boarding.

Taxiing to the runway.

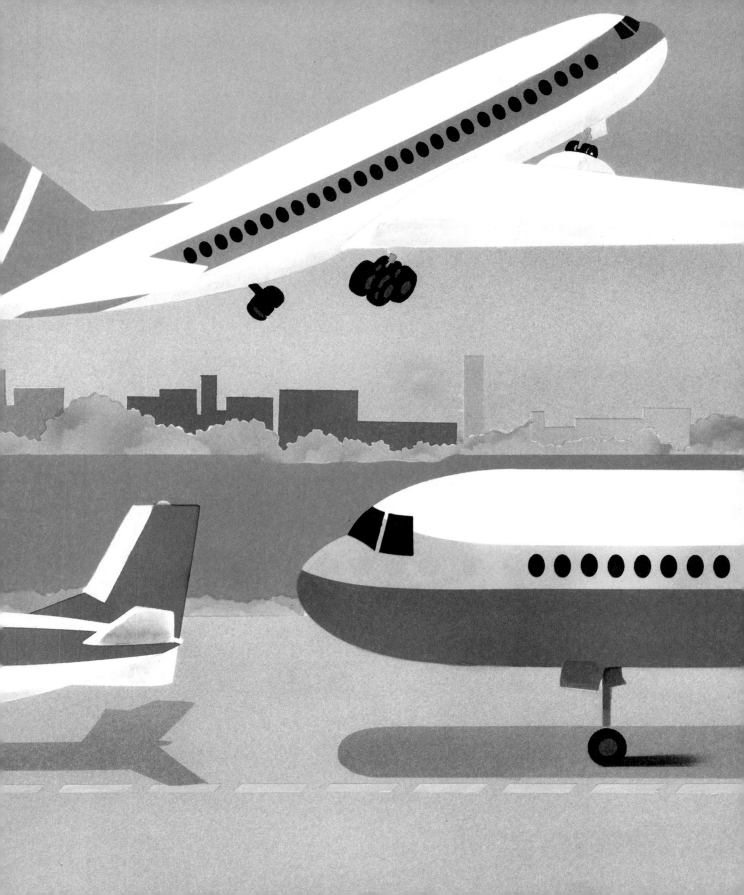

Ready.

Take off.

Flying over the airport.

Flying over the highways.

**Flying
over
rivers.**

Flying over cities.

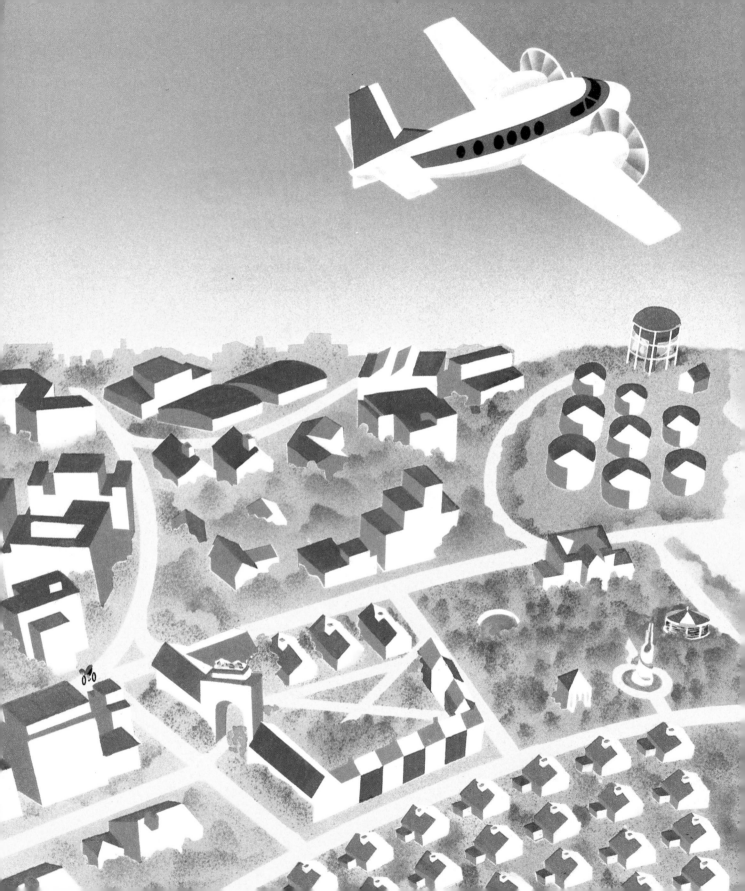

Flying across the country.

Flying high over mountains.

Flying
into the
clouds.

Flying over the clouds.

**Time
to head
down.**

There's
the
airport.

**Down,
down,
down.**

DOWN!

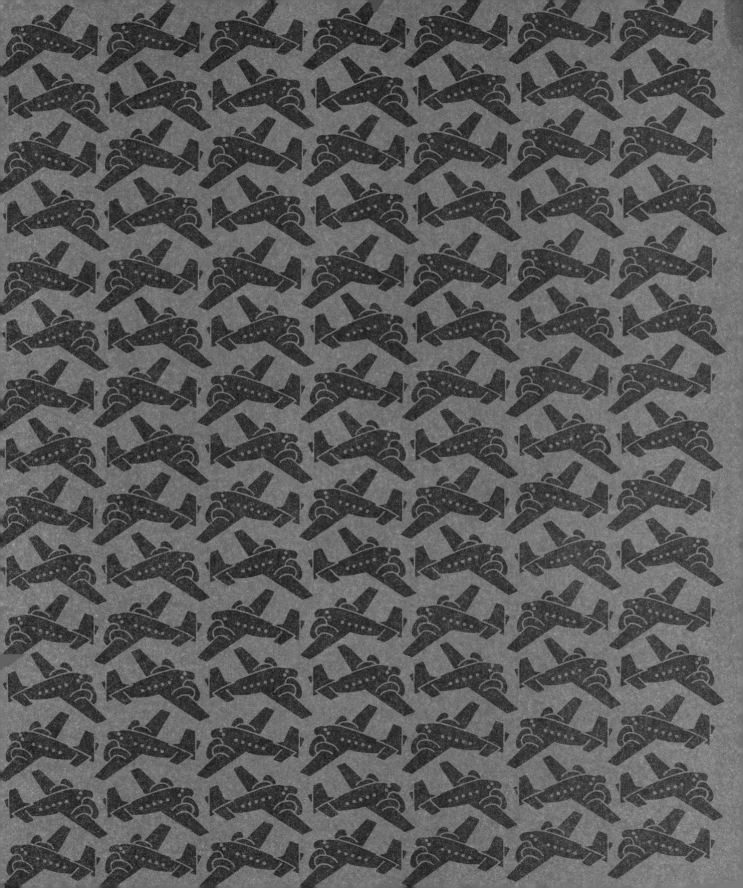